This book belongs to

....

Photographs courtesy of Shutterstock unless noted as follows:
Make Believe Ideas: 28bl (rocket), 28bl (microphone), 28bl (skateboard),
29tr (boxing glove), 29tr (beach ball), 29tl (spade), 29 br (socks).

This **PIG** can **FLY**

by Rosie Greening

make
believe
ideas

Get the most from this reader

Before reading:

- Look at the pictures and discuss them together. Ask questions such as, "What is the pig doing here?"

- Relate the topic to your child's world. For example, say: "Would you like to be able to fly? Why?"

- Familiarise your child with book vocabulary by using terms such as *word*, *letter*, *title*, *author* and *text*.

During reading:

- Prompt your child to sound out unknown words. Draw attention to neglected middle or end sounds.

- Encourage your child to use the pictures as clues to unknown words.

- Occasionally, ask what might happen next, and then check together as you read on.

- Monitor your child's understanding. Repeated readings can improve fluency and comprehension.

- Keep reading sessions short and enjoyable. Stop if your child becomes tired or frustrated.

• •

After reading:

- Discuss the book. Encourage your child to form opinions with questions such as, "What did you like best about this book?"

- Help your child work through the fun activities at the back of the book. Then ask him or her to reread the story. Praise any improvement.

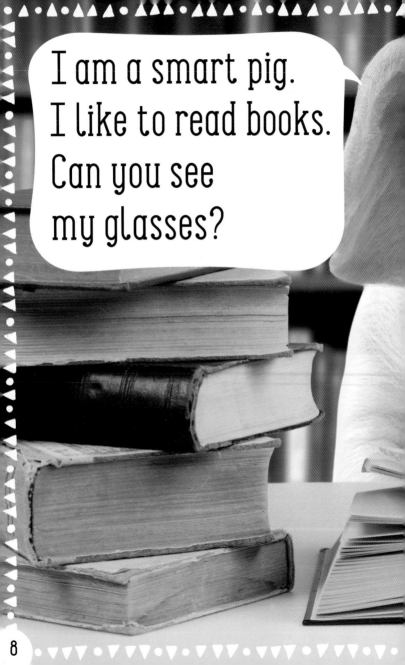

I am a smart pig.
I like to read books.
Can you see
my glasses?

8

I am an arty pig.
I like to paint pictures.
Can you see my brush?

I am a skiing pig.
I like to ski downhill.
Can you see my
red scarf?

I am a racing pig.
I like to race cars.
Can you see my number?

I am a flying pig.
I like to fly
across the sky.
Can you see
the clouds?

I am a sleeping pig.
Can you tell what
I am dreaming about?

Discussion Questions

1. When did the pig wear glasses?

2. What things did the pig dream about?

3. Do you think the pig liked the dream? Why?

❧ Sight Words ❧

Learning sight words helps you
read fluently. Practise these
sight words from the book.
Use them in sentences of your own.

can

read

am

see

to

like

my

you

23

ঌ Rhyming Words ঌ

Can you find the rhyming pairs?
Say them aloud.

pig

bee

red

jig

fed

see

smart

sky

fly

race

cart

face

Writing Practice

Read the words, and then trace them with your finger.

smart

read

ride

paint

ski

race

Silly Sentences

Have fun filling in the gap in each sentence. Use the ideas below or make up your own.

I am a .... pig.

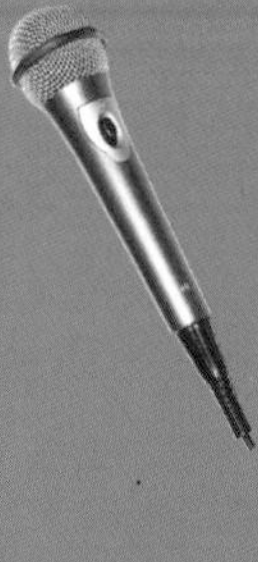

Can you see my ....?